Holt Spanish 1

Activities for Communication

HOLT, RINEHART AND WINSTON

A Harcourt Education Company

Orlando • **Austin** • New York • San Diego • Toronto • London

Reviewer

Mayanne Wright

ISBN 0-03-074411-3

2 3 4 5 6   170   06 05

Table of Contents

To the Teacher iv

COMMUNICATIVE ACTIVITIES

Capítulo 1
Vocabulario 1/Gramática 1 1A, 1B . . 1
Vocabulario 2/Gramática 2 2A, 2B . . 3

Capítulo 2
Vocabulario 1/Gramática 1 1A, 1B . . 5
Vocabulario 2/Gramática 2 2A, 2B . . 7

Capítulo 3
Vocabulario 1/Gramática 1 1A, 1B . . 9
Vocabulario 2/Gramática 2 2A, 2B . . 11

Capítulo 4
Vocabulario 1/Gramática 1 1A, 1B . . 13
Vocabulario 2/Gramática 2 2A, 2B . . 15

Capítulo 5
Vocabulario 1/Gramática 1 1A, 1B . . 17
Vocabulario 2/Gramática 2 2A, 2B . . 19

Capítulo 6
Vocabulario 1/Gramática 1 1A, 1B . . 21
Vocabulario 2/Gramática 2 2A, 2B . . 23

Capítulo 7
Vocabulario 1/Gramática 1 1A, 1B . . 25
Vocabulario 2/Gramática 2 2A, 2B . . 27

Capítulo 8
Vocabulario 1/Gramática 1 1A, 1B . . 29
Vocabulario 2/Gramática 2 2A, 2B . . 31

Capítulo 9
Vocabulario 1/Gramática 1 1A, 1B . . 33
Vocabulario 2/Gramática 2 2A, 2B . . 35

Capítulo 10
Vocabulario 1/Gramática 1 1A, 1B . . 37
Vocabulario 2/Gramática 2 2A, 2B . . 39

PICTURE SEQUENCES

Capítulo 1 43
Capítulo 2 44
Capítulo 3 45
Capítulo 4 46
Capítulo 5 47

Capítulo 6 48
Capítulo 7 49
Capítulo 8 50
Capítulo 9 51
Capítulo 10 52

INTERPERSONAL COMMUNICATION

Capítulo 1
Interviews 55
Role-Plays 56

Capítulo 2
Interviews 57
Role-Plays 58

Capítulo 3
Interviews 59
Role-Plays 60

Capítulo 4
Interviews 61
Role-Plays 62

Capítulo 5
Interviews 63
Role-Plays 64

Capítulo 6
Interviews 65
Role-Plays 66

Capítulo 7
Interviews 67
Role-Plays 68

Capítulo 8
Interviews 69
Role-Plays 70

Capítulo 9
Interviews 71
Role-Plays 72

Capítulo 10
Interviews 73
Role-Plays 74

iii

To the Teacher

Oral communication is the most challenging language skill to develop and test. The *¡Exprésate! Activities for Communication* book helps students develop their speaking skills and gives them opportunities to communicate in many different situations. The Communicative Activities and Interpersonal Communication Cards provide a variety of information-gap activities, role-plays, and interviews to assist students with the progression from closed-ended practice to more creative, open-ended use of Spanish. The Picture Sequences provide image-based scenarios that allow students to creatively incorporate learned vocabulary, grammar, and functions from each chapter while working in pairs or groups. With the focus on conversation and real-life context, the activities in this book will help your students achieve the goal of genuine interaction, as well as prepare them for the oral exam following each chapter test and the oral assessment items in the Alternative Assessment section of the *Assessment Program*.

Each chapter of *Activities for Communication* provides:

Communicative Activities In each of the ten chapters, two communicative, pair-work activities encourage students to use Spanish in realistic conversation, in settings where they must seek and share information. The activities provide cooperative language practice and encourage students to take risks with language in a relaxed, uninhibiting, and enjoyable setting. The activities correspond to each vocabulary and grammar section and encourage use of functions, vocabulary, and grammar presented in that chapter section. Each activity may be used upon completion of each grammar and vocabulary section to promote oral proficiency and to prepare students for oral assessment; this could be for the oral exam following each chapter, and/or the oral performance and portfolio activities in the Alternative Assessment section of the *Assessment Program*. The activities may also be recorded on audio or video tape for inclusion in students' portfolios, or may be used as an informal review of each section to provide additional oral practice.

Picture Sequences Each of the ten chapters contains one picture sequence activity that provides a chapter-oriented story for students to work on in pairs or groups. The picture sequences are designed to guide students, within the context of a chapter-themed story, to creatively integrate and use chapter vocabulary, grammar, and functions. Each picture sequence may be used upon completion of the chapter as a global performance assessment, or may be used to prepare students for the picture sequence assessment activity in the Alternative Assessment portion of the *Assessment Program*. The stories may also be recorded on audio or video tape for inclusion in students' portfolios. Rubrics for grading the picture stories are available in the Alternative Assessment portion of the *Assessment Program*.

Interpersonal Communication Cards Each of the ten chapters contains three interviews and three situations for role-playing, one for each grammar and vocabulary section and one global review for the entire chapter, in blackline master form. These cards are designed to stimulate conversation and to prepare students for the oral exam following the chapter test, as well as for the oral performance and portfolio activities in the Alternative Assessment section of the *Assessment Program*. (Rubrics for grading these activities are available in the Alternative Assessment portion of the *Assessment Program*.) The interviews or role-playing may be used as pair work with the entire class, as activities to begin the class period, as oral performance assessments upon completion of each chapter section, and as a review of each chapter. They may also be used to encourage oral practice at any point during the study of each section. These conversations may be recorded as audio or video additions to students' portfolios. Because the cards may be recycled throughout the scholastic year as review of chapters already completed, students will be rewarded as they realize they are meeting goals and improving their communicative abilities. To avoid having to copy the cards repeatedly, consider mounting them on cardboard and laminating them. They may be filed for use during the year as well as for future classes.

(**v**)

¡Empecemos!

SITUATION You are participating in an International Student Forum. The organizing committee has asked a volunteer to check off the participants as they arrive.

TASK 1 As the volunteer, greet the participants (your partner), and ask them their names and where they are from. Listen to the answers and write each participant's country under his or her name.

MODELO A — Buenas tardes.
B — Buenas tardes.
A — ¿Cómo te llamas?
B — Me llamo Angélica Martínez.
A — ¿De dónde eres tú?
B — Yo soy de Estados Unidos.

Angélica Martínez
Estados Unidos

Pilar Rodríguez
_____

Juan Garza
_____

Miguelito Gutiérrez
_____

TASK 2 Now, switch roles. Pretend you are the following participants and answer your partner's questions.

Santiago Talavera Elena Vega Rosa Pérez
Cuba España Puerto Rico

1

¡Empecemos!

SITUATION You are participating in an International Student Forum. The organizing committee has asked a volunteer to check off the participants as they arrive.

TASK 1 Your partner is a volunteer working for the forum. Pretend you are the following participants and answer your partner's questions.

MODELO   A — Buenas tardes.
B — Buenas tardes.
A — ¿Cómo te llamas?
B — Me llamo Angélica Martínez.
A — ¿De dónde eres tú?
B — Yo soy de Estados Unidos.

Angélica Martínez
Estados Unidos

Pilar Rodríguez   Juan Garza   Miguelito Gutiérrez
España   Cuba   Puerto Rico

TASK 2 Now, switch roles. As the volunteer, greet the participants (your partner), and ask them their names and where they are from. Listen to the answers and write each participant's country under his or her name.

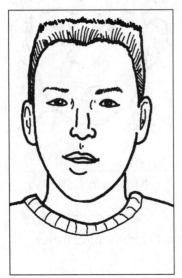  

Santiago Talavera   Rosa Pérez   Elena Vega

_____   _____   _____

Activities for Communication

¡Empecemos!

COMMUNICATIVE ACTIVITY 2A

SITUATION You and your partner are compiling a contact list with the names, phone numbers, and e-mail addresses of your classmates.

TASK 1 Give your partner the information below and spell out names and e-mail addresses as requested.

MODELO   B — ¿Cómo se llama?

A — Se llama Emilia.

B — ¿Cómo se escribe *Emilia*?

A — Se escribe e-eme-i-ele-i-a.

B — ¿Cuál es el teléfono de Emilia?

A — Es siete-uno-tres-dos-cinco-dos-nueve.

B — ¿Cuál es el correo electrónico de ella?

A — Es e-eme-i-ele-i-a arroba zeta-i-pe-i punto e-ese.

Gladys	7-16-28-22	gladys28@red.com
Jorge	9-22-30-19	jortega@atn.pr
Rosaura	2-13-24-15	rosa03@bst.cl

TASK 2 Now, switch roles. Ask your partner how to spell your classmates' names and what their telephone numbers and e-mail addresses are. Then write down what your partner says.

Nombre	Teléfono	Correo electrónico
Emilia	7-13-25-29	emilia@zipi.es

3

¡Empecemos!

SITUATION You and your partner are compiling a contact list with the names, phone numbers, and e-mail addresses of your classmates.

TASK 1 Ask your partner how to spell your classmates' names and what their telephone numbers and e-mail addresses are. Then write down what your partner says.

MODELO B — ¿Cómo se llama?
A — Se llama Emilia.
B — ¿Cómo se escribe *Emilia*?
A — Se escribe e-eme-i-ele-i-a.
B — ¿Cuál es el teléfono de Emilia?
A — Es siete-uno-tres-dos-cinco-dos-nueve.
B — ¿Cuál es el correo electrónico de ella?
A — Es e-eme-i-ele-i-a arroba zeta-i-pe-i punto e-ese.

Nombre	Teléfono	Correo electrónico
Emilia	7-13-25-29	emilia@zipi.es

TASK 2 Now, switch roles. Give your partner the information below and spell out names and e-mail addresses as requested.

Teresa	5-31-15-22	teresa06@atn.mx
Federico	3-17-24-09	Fede16@red.es
Jaime	8-23-19-30	jaimito@int.do

A conocernos

SITUATION You and your partner are looking for new cyber friends in your school's online chat room. You would like to make friends with people who have the same interests as you.

TASK 1 Your partner opened a chat room on your school's online network. Go over the list and ask your partner questions about each user to decide whether you would like to make friends with him or her.

MODELO A — ¿Cómo es Julieta?
B — Julieta es extrovertida y romántica.
A — ¿Cuándo es su cumpleaños?
B — Es el 29 de diciembre.

Chat Room Listings—PALO ALTO HIGH SCHOOL		
Nombre	**Descripción**	**Cumpleaños**
Julieta	extrovertida, romántica	29 de diciembre
Rebeca		
Diana		
Felipe		

TASK 2 Now, switch roles and answer your partner's questions. Decide with your partner who will be your new cyber friends.

Chat Room Listings—PALO ALTO HIGH SCHOOL		
Nombre	**Descripción**	**Cumpleaños**
Magda	bonita, graciosa	5 de febrero
Gerardo	aburrido, bajo	7 de octubre
Nancy	intelectual, trabajadora	15 de agosto

5

A conocernos

SITUATION You and your partner are looking for new cyber friends in your school's online chat room. You would like to make friends with people who have the same interests as you.

TASK 1 You opened a chat room listing on your school's online network. Go over the list with your partner and answer his or her questions. Then, decide together who will be your new cyber friends.

MODELO A — ¿Cómo es Julieta?
B — Julieta es extrovertida y romántica.
A — ¿Cuándo es su cumpleaños?
B — Es el 29 de diciembre.

Chat Room Listings—PALO ALTO HIGH SCHOOL		
Nombre	**Descripción**	**Cumpleaños**
Julieta	extrovertida, romántica	29 de diciembre
Rebeca	atlética, tímida	14 de septiembre
Diana	pelirroja, simpática	7 de abril
Felipe	intelectual, serio	13 de julio

TASK 2 Now, switch roles. Ask your partner questions about each user to decide whether you would like to make friends with him or her.

Chat Room Listings—PALO ALTO HIGH SCHOOL		
Nombre	**Descripción**	**Cumpleaños**
Magda		
Gerardo		
Nancy		

A conocernos

SITUATION You are taking a survey about the foods and activities that teenagers in your area like and dislike.

TASK 1 Ask your partner for information about which foods and activities he/she likes and why.

MODELO   A — ¿Te gusta la pizza?
B — Sí, me gusta la pizza.
A — ¿Por qué te gusta la pizza?
B — Me gusta porque es deliciosa.

_____   _____   _____   _____

_____   _____   _____   _____

TASK 2 Now, switch roles. Answer your partner's questions about which foods and activities you like and why. Remember to use the correct adjective and verb forms.

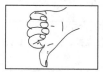   

aburrido   formidable   divertido   bueno

Holt Spanish 1   Activities for Communication

A conocernos

COMMUNICATIVE ACTIVITY 2B

SITUATION You are answering a survey about the foods and activities that teenagers in your area like and dislike.

TASK 1 Answer your partner's questions about which foods and activities you like and why. Remember to use the correct adjective and verb forms.

MODELO A — ¿Te gusta la pizza?
B — Sí, me gusta la pizza.
A — ¿Por qué te gusta la pizza?
B — Me gusta porque es deliciosa.

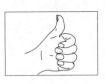

  interesante   pésimo   fenomenal   delicioso

TASK 2 Now, switch roles. Ask your partner about which foods and activities he/she likes and why.

_____   _____   _____   _____

_____   _____   _____   _____

¿Qué te gusta hacer?

SITUATION You and your partner are planning a weekend retreat for your Spanish class. You have both asked several classmates what they like to do. Now, share with each other the information that you gathered in order to plan activities that everyone will enjoy.

TASK 1 Ask your partner about the classmates he or she interviewed.

MODELO A — ¿Qué le gusta hacer a Carmen?
B — A ella le gusta correr y jugar al básquetbol.

Nombre	Le gusta(n)...
Carmen	correr y jugar al básquetbol
Ana	
Alejandro	
Paco	

TASK 2 Now, respond to your partner's questions about the classmates that you interviewed.

Nombre	Le gusta(n)...
Carlos	patinar y jugar al fútbol
Isabel	ir de compras y escuchar música
Sabrina	dibujar y jugar al volibol

¿Qué te gusta hacer?

SITUATION You and your partner are planning a weekend retreat for your Spanish class. You have both asked several classmates what they like to do. Now, share with each other the information that you gathered in order to plan activities that everyone will enjoy.

TASK 1 Respond to your partner's questions about the classmates that you interviewed.

MODELO   A — ¿Qué le gusta hacer a Carmen?
B — A ella le gusta correr y jugar al básquetbol.

Nombre	Le gusta(n)...
Carmen	correr y jugar al básquetbol
Ana	alquilar videos y patinar
Alejandro	leer y jugar al béisbol
Paco	cantar y ver televisión

TASK 2 Now, ask your partner about the classmates he or she interviewed.

Nombre	Le gusta(n)...
Carlos	
Isabel	
Sabrina	

¿Qué te gusta hacer?

SITUATION You and your partner are discussing what you, your friends, and your family do on the weekend.

TASK 1 Ask your partner about what the following people do on the weekend.

MODELO A — ¿Qué hace tu amiga Patricia los fines de semana?
B — Patricia va a la playa los fines de semana.
A — ¿Con qué frecuencia va ella a la playa?
B — Ella va a veces.

¿Quién?	¿Qué hace(s)?	¿Con qué frecuencia?
Patricia	ir / playa	a veces
tu hermano		
María		
tú		

TASK 2 Now, switch roles and answer your partner's questions about the following people.

¿Quién?	¿Qué hace(n)?	¿Con qué frecuencia?
mi familia	ir / parque	casi siempre
Francisca y Nilda	ir / colegio	(casi) nunca
Pedro	jugar / volibol	a veces

¿Qué te gusta hacer?

COMMUNICATIVE ACTIVITY 2B

SITUATION You and your partner are discussing what you, your friends, and your family do on the weekend.

TASK 1 Answer your partner's questions about what you and the following people do on the weekend.

MODELO A — ¿Qué hace tu amiga Patricia los fines de semana?
B — Patricia va a la playa los fines de semana.
A — ¿Con qué frecuencia va ella a la playa?
B — Ella va a veces.

¿Quién?	¿Qué hace(s)?	¿Con qué frecuencia?
Patricia	ir / playa	a veces
mi hermano	jugar / ajedrez	(casi) siempre
María	tocar / piano	a veces
yo	ir / cine	(casi) nunca

TASK 2 Now, switch roles and ask your partner what the following people do on the weekend.

¿Quién?	¿Qué hace(n)?	¿Con qué frecuencia?
tu familia		
Francisca y Nilda		
Pedro		

(12)

La vida escolar

SITUATION You and your partner have just started school and are making sure that you have all the necessary school supplies for your first day of classes.

TASK 1 Ask your partner what classes he or she has on Mondays in the morning. Then, find out which school supplies are needed for each class.

MODELO A — ¿Qué clase tienes primero los lunes?
B — Primero tengo español.
A — ¿Qué necesitas para la clase de español?
B — Necesito lápices.
A — ¿Qué clase tienes después de español?
B — Después tengo...

Hora	Materia	Útiles escolares
7:50	español	lápices
8:45		
9:40		
10:35		
11:30		

TASK 2 Now, answer your partner's questions about your Monday morning classes.

Hora	Materia	Útiles escolares
8:45	francés	muchas carpetas
9:40	computación	una computadora
10:35	matemáticas	una regla
11:30	inglés	un cuaderno

(13)

La vida escolar

SITUATION You and your partner have just started school and are making sure that you have all the necessary school supplies for your first day of classes.

TASK 1 Answer your parter's questions about your Monday morning classes.

MODELO A — ¿Qué clase tienes primero los lunes?
    B — Primero tengo español.
    A — ¿Qué necesitas para la clase de español?
    B — Necesito lápices.
    A — ¿Qué clase tienes después de español?
    B — Después tengo...

Hora	Materia	Útiles escolares
7:50	español	lápices
8:45	historia	dos cuadernos
9:40	biología	bolígrafos
10:35	alemán	un diccionario
11:30	educación física	un reloj

TASK 2 Now, switch roles and ask your partner what classes he or she has Monday mornings. Then, find out which school supplies are needed for each class.

Hora	Materia	Útiles escolares
8:45		
9:40		
10:35		
11:30		

La vida escolar

SITUATION You and a friend (your partner) are making plans to hang out together during the next two weeks.

TASK 1 Invite your partner to this week's events. Try to find at least two activities that you can do together.

MODELO A — Hay un partido de fútbol el lunes a las 4:45. ¿Quieres ir conmigo?

B — No, tengo que estudiar los lunes por la tarde.

Día	Evento o Plan
lunes	un partido de fútbol a las 4:45
martes	un partido de béisbol a las 5:00
miércoles	ir de compras a las 4:30
jueves	ir a la biblioteca a las 4:00
viernes	un concierto en el auditorio a las 7:00
sábado	ir al cine a las 6:15

TASK 2 Now, switch roles. For each invitation, check your datebook for next week to see if you're free. Decline an invitation if you're not free and tell why you can't go. If you are free, accept or decline an invitation by choosing a sentence listed in the box below. Pencil in any invitations that you accept.

Día	Agenda
lunes	ir al ensayo en el auditorio
martes	
miércoles	ir a la biblioteca por la tarde
jueves	
viernes	hacer ejercicio en el gimnasio por la tarde
sábado	

> **No tengo ganas.**
> **Sí, no tengo planes.**
> **¡Claro que sí!**

La vida escolar

SITUATION You and a friend (your partner) are making plans to hang out together during the next two weeks.

TASK 1 For each invitation, check your datebook for this week to see if you're free. Decline an invitation if you're not free and tell why you can't go. If you are free, accept or decline an invitation by choosing a sentence listed in the box below. Pencil in any invitations that you accept.

MODELO A — Hay un partido de fútbol el lunes a las 4:45. ¿Quieres ir conmigo?

B — No, tengo que estudiar los lunes por la tarde.

Día	Agenda
lunes	estudiar por la tarde
martes	
miércoles	correr en el estadio del colegio por la tarde
jueves	
viernes	salir a comer con mi familia por la noche
sábado	

> No tengo ganas.
> Sí, no tengo planes.
> ¡Claro que sí!

TASK 2 Now, switch roles. Invite your partner to next week's events. Try to find at least two activities that you can do together.

lunes	un partido de volibol a las 4:45
martes	un partido de básquetbol a las 5:15
miércoles	ir al centro comercial a las 4:00
jueves	una reunión del club de español a las 3:30
viernes	ir a una fiesta de baile a las 6:00
sábado	un concierto de piano a las 7:00

16

En casa con la familia

COMMUNICATIVE ACTIVITY 1A

SITUATION You and a friend (your partner) went to a birthday party at your friend Rosa's house last night. You are talking about the people that you met.

TASK 1 You only remember physical characteristics of some of the people you met last night. Describe the following people to your partner. After your partner tells the person's relationship to Rosa, ask him or her for the person's name. Fill in the chart below with your partner's answers.

MODELO A — Él tiene el pelo negro, ojos negros y es muy alto.
B — Es el padre de Rosa.
A — ¿Cómo se llama?
B — Sr. Caballeros.

Nombre	Sr. Caballeros			
Relación	el padre de Rosa			
Descripción	pelo negro, ojos verdes, alto	pelo negro, ojos verdes, usa lentes	ojos de color café, pelo corto, muy joven	pelo canoso, baja, ciega

TASK 2 Now, switch roles. Your partner only remembers physical characteristics of some of the people he or she met last night. Listen as he or she describes certain people. Then, tell your partner each person's relationship to Rosa and his or her name.

Nombre	Sra. Caballeros	Mario	Sr. Almagro
Relación	la madre de Rosa	el hermano menor de Rosa	el abuelo de Rosa
Descripción	pelo corto, ojos de color café, alta	ojos de color café, sordo, delgado	ojos negros, pelo canoso, alto

CAPÍTULO

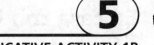

En casa con la familia

COMMUNICATIVE ACTIVITY 1B

SITUATION You and a friend (your partner) went to a birthday party at your friend Rosa's house last night. You are talking about the people that you met.

TASK 1 Your partner only remembers physical characteristics of some of the people he or she met last night. Listen as he or she describes certain people. Then, tell your partner each person's relationship to Rosa and his or her name.

MODELO   A — Él tiene el pelo negro, ojos negros y es muy alto.
            B — Es el padre de Rosa.
            A — ¿Cómo se llama?
            B — Sr. Caballeros.

Nombre	Sr. Caballeros	Fernando	Juana	Sra. Almagro
Relación	el padre de Rosa	el tío de Rosa	la hermana de Rosa	la abuela de Rosa
Descripción	pelo negro, ojos negros, alto	pelo negro, ojos verdes, usa lentes	ojos de color café, pelo corto, muy joven	pelo canoso, baja, ciega

TASK 2 Now, switch roles. You only remember physical characteristics of some of the people you met last night. Describe the following people to your partner. After your partner tells the person's relationship to Rosa, ask him or her for the person's name. Fill in the chart below with your partner's answers.

Nombre			
Relación			
Descripción	pelo corto, ojos de color café, alta	ojos de color café, sordo, delgado	ojos negros, pelo canoso, alto

18

En casa con la familia

SITUATION You and your partner are discussing who is responsible for which chores in each of your families.

TASK 1 Ask your partner what his or her family members do to help out at home. Then, ask your partner what each family member thinks about that chore. Fill in the chart below with your partner's answers.

MODELO   A — ¿Qué hace tu mamá para ayudar en casa?
B — A mi mamá le toca lavar los platos.
A — ¿Qué le parece a ella?
B — A ella le parece bien.

mi mamá
bien

¿Quién?	Quehacer	¿Qué le parece?
tu mamá	lavar los platos	A ella le parece bien.
tú		
tu hermana menor		
tu abuelo		

TASK 2 Now, switch roles. Respond to your partner's questions about your family.

yo
una lata

mi hermana y yo
aburrido

mi papá
bien

(19)

En casa con la familia

SITUATION You and your partner are discussing who is responsible for which chores in each of your families.

TASK 1 Answer your partner's questions about your family. First, tell him or her what each family member's chore is. Then, tell your partner what he or she thinks about that chore.

MODELO   A — ¿Qué hace tu mamá para ayudar en casa?
B — A mi mamá le toca lavar los platos.
A — ¿Qué le parece a ella?
B — A ella le parece bien.

mi mamá
bien

yo
injusto

mi hermana menor
mal

mi abuelo
muy bien

TASK 2 Now, switch roles. Ask your partner what his or her family members do to help out at home. Then, ask what each family member thinks about that chore. Fill in the chart below with your partner's answers.

¿Quién?	Quehacer	¿Qué le parece?
tú		
tu hermana y tú		
tu papá		

(20)

CAPÍTULO

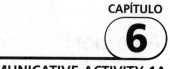

¡A comer!

COMMUNICATIVE ACTIVITY 1A

SITUATION You and your partner are looking over your menus in the restaurant Buena Vista. Your partner can't decide on what to eat or drink today, even though he or she comes often to this restaurant.

TASK 1 Help your partner decide on what to order by asking him or her if he or she likes the ingredients in the chart below. Then, suggest an item on the menu that contains that ingredient. Continue making suggestions to your partner until he or she decides on an entrée and a drink.

MODELO A — ¿Te gustan las papas?
B — ¡Sí, me encantan!
Son muy ricas.
A — ¿Qué tal si pruebas
las papas fritas de aquí?
B — No, siempre están
frías y horribles.

ingrediente	plato
las papas encantar, muy rico(a)	las papas fritas estar frío(a) y horrible(s)

ingrediente	plato (dish) o bebida (drink)
el queso	la hamburguesa con queso
el atún	la ensalada de atún
el tomate	la sopa de tomate
la naranja	el jugo de naranja

TASK 2 Now, switch roles. Answer your partner's questions according to your comments listed below. Your partner will continue making suggestions until you decide on an entrée and a drink.

ingrediente / plato o bebida	comentario del ingrediente	comentario del plato o bebida
las verduras/ la sopa de verduras	no gustar, ser picante	estar frío(a)
el jamón/ el sándwich de jamón con queso	gustar, ser riquísimo(a)	siempre estar delicioso(a)
el atún/ el sandwich de atún	gustar, ser bueno(a)	a veces estar un poco salado(a)
el tomate/ el jugo de tomate	encantar, ser delicioso(a)	estar rico(a)

(21)

¡A comer!

COMMUNICATIVE ACTIVITY 1B

SITUATION You and your partner are looking over your menus in the restaurant Buena Vista. You can't decide on what to eat or drink today, even though you come often to this restaurant.

TASK 1 Your partner helps you order by suggesting certain menu items. Answer his or her questions according to your comments listed below. Your partner will continue making suggestions until you decide on an entrée and a drink.

MODELO A — ¿Te gustan las papas?
B — ¡Sí, me encantan!
Son muy ricas.
A — ¿Qué tal si pruebas
las papas fritas de aquí?
B — No, siempre están
frías y horribles.

ingrediente	plato
las papas	las papas fritas
encantar,	estar frío(a) y
muy rico(a)	horrible(s)

ingrediente /plato *(dish)* o bebida *(drink)*	comentario del ingrediente	comentario del plato o bebida
el queso / la hamburguesa con queso	encantar, ser riquísimo(a)	estar horrible
el atún / la ensalada de atún	no gustar, ser rico(a)	estar salado(a)
el tomate / la sopa de tomate	gustar, ser bueno(a)	estar riquísimo(a)
la naranja / el jugo de naranja	encantar, ser delicioso(a)	estar muy bueno(a)

TASK 2 Now, switch roles. Ask your partner if he or she likes the ingredients in the chart below. Then, suggest an item on the menu that contains that ingredient. Continue making suggestions to your partner until he or she decides on an entrée and a drink.

ingrediente	plato o bebida
las verduras	la sopa de verduras
el jamón	el sándwich de jamón con queso
el atún	el sándwich de atún
el tomate	el jugo de tomate

¡A comer!

COMMUNICATIVE ACTIVITY 2A

SITUATION You and your brothers and sisters are at home alone tonight and have to prepare dinner. You are the oldest and have been named the chef of the house.

TASK 1 You and your younger sibling (your partner) are in the kitchen looking for food to prepare. Ask what food there is. Then, tell your partner what he or she can do with each food to help prepare the meal.

MODELO A — ¿Qué hay de comida?
B — Tenemos manzanas.
A — Sácalas del refrigerador.
B — ¿Puedo ayudar más?
A — Sí, ponlas en un plato hondo.

lista de comida	para ayudar
las manzanas	sacar del refrigerador / poner en un plato hondo
las zanahorias	cortar con el cuchillo / mezclar en una ensalada
el pollo	sacar del refrigerador / poner en el horno
el maíz	limpiar con agua fría / poner en un plato

TASK 2 Now, switch roles. Answer your partner's question by telling him or her each of the foods you have according to the list below. After he or she tells you what to do with each food, ask your partner what else you can do to help.

¡A comer!

SITUATION You and your brothers and sisters are at home alone tonight and have to prepare dinner. Your older sibling (your partner) is the chef of the house.

TASK 1 You and your older sibling (your partner) are in the kitchen looking for food to prepare. Answer your partner's question by telling him or her each of the foods you have below. After he or she tells you what to do with each food, ask your partner what else you can do to help.

MODELO   A — ¿Qué hay de comida?
B — Tenemos manzanas.
A — Sácalas del refrigerador.
B — ¿Puedo ayudar más?
A — Sí, ponlas en un plato hondo.

TASK 2 Now, switch roles. Ask your younger sibling what food there is. Then, say what he or she can do with each food to help prepare the meal.

lista de comida	para ayudar
el queso	sacar del refrigerador / poner en la mesa
las papas	limpiar con agua / cortar y poner en el horno
el pan	cortar / poner en la mesa

Cuerpo sano, mente sana

COMMUNICATIVE ACTIVITY 1A

SITUATION You and your friend (your partner) are comparing your typical morning routines.

TASK 1 Ask your partner when he or she does the following activities. Then, ask what he or she has to do after each activity. Take notes.

MODELO A — ¿Cuándo te bañas?
B — Me baño después de quitarme el piyama.
A — ¿Qué tienes que hacer después de bañarte?
B — Me peino el pelo.

Actividad	¿Cuándo?	¿Y después...?
bañarte	después de quitarte el piyama	te peinas el pelo
lavarte los dientes		
vestirte		
levantarte		

TASK 2 Now, answer your partner's questions about your routine. When he or she asks when you do an activity, respond by using the following chart.

Por la mañana, tengo que...	
1.	despertarme muy temprano
2.	levantarme
3.	quitarme el piyama
4.	bañarme en 10 minutos
5.	peinarme el pelo
6.	secarme el pelo
7.	vestirme
8.	despertar a mis padres
9.	desayunar pan tostado
10.	salir para el colegio

Cuerpo sano, mente sana

SITUATION You and your friend (your partner) are comparing your typical morning routines.

TASK 1 Answer your partner's questions about your routine. When he or she asks when you do an activity, respond by using the following chart.

MODELO A — ¿Cuándo te bañas?
B — Me baño después de quitarme el piyama.
A — ¿Qué tienes que hacer después de bañarte?
B — Me peino el pelo.

Por la mañana, tengo que...	
1.	despertarme temprano
2.	levantarme
3.	quitarme el piyama
4.	bañarme en 10 minutos
5.	peinarme el pelo
6.	vestirme rápidamente
7.	vestir a mis hermanos menores
8.	desayunar huevos y tocino
9.	lavarme los dientes
10.	salir para el colegio

TASK 2 Now, switch roles. Ask your partner when he or she does the following activities. Then, ask what he or she has to do after each activity. Take notes.

Actividad	¿Cuándo?	¿Y después...?
levantarte		
secarte el pelo		
desayunar		

26

Cuerpo sano, mente sana

SITUATION Both you and your friend (your partner) have been feeling under the weather lately.

TASK 1 Ask your partner what is wrong with him or her. After your partner tells you his or her concern, offer advice. Use the verbs below to give one affirmative informal command and one negative informal command for each concern.

MODELO A — ¿Qué te pasa?
B — Siempre me siento cansado(a).
A — Acuéstate más temprano.
B — Bueno, ¿y qué más?
A — ¡No vuelvas tarde a casa!

Affirmative commands	Negative commands
acostarse más temprano	volver tarde a casa
estudiar más	tener miedo
dormir lo suficiente	trabajar tanto
comer bien	comprar dulces
descansar un poco	ver tanta televisión

TASK 2 Now you are the one feeling unhealthy. Answer your partner's questions about the way you feel by using the concerns listed below. Write down the advice that he or she gives you.

Asuntos (*concerns*)	Consejos
siempre estar enfermo(a)	
tener sueño	
dolerle las piernas	
no sentirse bien	
dolerle la cabeza	

CAPÍTULO

Cuerpo sano, mente sana

COMMUNICATIVE ACTIVITY 2B

SITUATION Both you and your friend (your partner) have been feeling under the weather lately.

TASK 1 Answer your partner's questions about the way you feel by using the concerns listed below. Write down the advice that he or she gives you.

MODELO A — ¿Qué te pasa?
B — Siempre me siento cansado(a).
A — Acuéstate más temprano.
B — Bueno, ¿y qué más?
A — ¡No vuelvas tarde a casa!

Asuntos *(concerns)*	Consejos
siempre sentirse cansado(a)	
estar nervioso(a)	
tener catarro	
dolerle el estómago	
dolerle los ojos	

TASK 2 Now, switch roles. Ask your partner what is wrong with him or her. After your partner tells you his or her concern, offer advice. Use the verbs below to give one affirmative informal command and one negative informal command.

Affirmative commands	Negative commands
comer frutas	fumar
hacer ejercicio	salir todas las noches
estirarse	correr
dormir hasta tarde	ver tanta televisión
relajarse	leer tanto

Activities for Communication

Vamos de compras

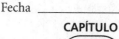

SITUATION You and a friend (your partner) are shopping for clothes together.

TASK 1 Ask your friend what he or she thinks about an article of clothing you've just tried on. Then, point to a similar item and ask whether he or she prefers it to the first item. Circle the color of the item that your friend prefers and write his or her reason.

MODELO
A — ¿Qué te parecen los pantalones cortos?
B — Me gustan. Te quedan bien.
A — ¿Prefieres estos pantalones cortos blancos o esos pantalones cortos grises?
B — Prefiero esos pantalones cortos grises. Son más bonitos que estos pantalones cortos blancos.

blancos / grises
más bonitos

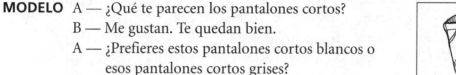

negra / morada   café / verde   blancos / negros   azules / rojos

TASK 2 Now, your partner asks you to comment on and compare the clothes he or she is trying on. Respond to your partner's questions according to the chart below.

Ropa	Color	Comentarios	Preferencias
la camiseta	roja	no me gusta / parecer pasado(a) de moda	
	anaranjada		✓mejor
las botas	negras	me encantan / bonitos(as)	✓bonitos(as) y más baratos(as)
	verdes		
el abrigo	azul	costar 200 dólares / muy caro(a)	
	blanco		✓mejor y menos caro(a)
los pantalones	morados	me gustan / quedar bien	
	amarillos		✓quedar mejor

(29)

Vamos de compras

SITUATION You and a friend (your partner) are shopping for clothes together.

TASK 1 Your partner asks you to comment on and compare the clothes he or she is trying on. Respond to your partner's questions according to the chart below.

MODELO A — ¿Qué te parecen los pantalones cortos?
B — Me gustan. Te quedan bien.
A — ¿Prefieres estos pantalones cortos blancos
o esos pantalones cortos grises?
B — Prefiero esos pantalones cortos grises. Son más bonitos que estos pantalones cortos blancos.

blancos / grises
más bonitos

Ropa	Color	Comentarios	Preferencias
la chaqueta	negra	es bonito(a), pero quedar grande	
	morada		✓más barato(a)
el suéter	café	me parece bien / a la última moda	✓es mejor
	verde		
los zapatos de tenis	blancos	costar 150 dólares / muy caros(as)	
	negros		✓menos caros(as)
los calcetines	azules	me gustan / baratos(as)	✓quedar mejor
	rojos		

TASK 2 Now, switch roles. Ask your partner what he or she thinks about an article of clothing you've just tried on. Then, point to a similar item and ask whether he or she prefers it to the first item. Circle the color of the item that your friend prefers and write his or her reason.

| roja / anaranjada | negras / verdes | azul / blanco | morados / amarillos |

_____   _____   _____   _____

Nombre _____ Clase _____ Fecha _____

Vamos de compras

SITUATION Your family and your partner's family are close friends. You are throwing a birthday party for a friend you have in common. Everyone in both families is helping to prepare for the party.

TASK 1 Your partner's family took care of their responsibilities yesterday. Below is your partner's list of things to do but you can't read who did or bought what. Find out who went to the following places and what they did there.

MODELO A — ¿Quién fue a la juguetería ayer?
B — Mi hermano fue a la juguetería.
A — ¿Qué compró?
B — Compró un juego de mesa.

¿Quién fue?	Lo que hizo
su hermano	ir a la juguetería a comprar <u>un juego de mesa</u>
	ir a la tienda de música a comprar_____
	ir a la librería a comprar _____
	ir a la heladería a comprar _____

TASK 2 Now your partner wants to know who in your family went where and what they bought. Your partner is looking at your family's list of things to do from last weekend, but can't read who did or bought what. Answer his or her questions.

Persona	¿Adónde?	¿Qué hizo?
mi padre y hermano	ir a la joyería	comprar un anillo y una pulsera
yo	ir a la zapatería	comprar unas sandalias
mi hermana	ir a la librería	comprar una revista de tiras cómicas

(31)

Vamos de compras

SITUATION Your family and your partner's family are close friends. You are throwing a birthday party for a friend you have in common. Everyone in both families is helping to prepare for the party.

TASK 1 Your family took care of their responsibilities yesterday. Your partner is looking at your list of things to do but can't make out who did or bought what. Answer his or her questions according to the chart below.

MODELO A — ¿Quién fue a la juguetería ayer?
B — Mi hermano fue a la juguetería.
A — ¿Qué compró?
B — Compró un juego de mesa.

Persona	¿Adónde?	¿Qué hizo?
mi hermano	ir a la juguetería	comprar un juego de mesa
mi mamá	ir a la tienda de música	comprar unos discos compactos
yo	ir a la librería	comprar una tarjeta de cumpleaños
mi papá y mamá	ir a la heladería	comprar el helado

TASK 2 Your partner's family took care of their responsibilities last weekend. Below is your partner's list of things to do but you can't read who did or bought what. Find out who went to the following places and what they did there.

¿Quién fue?	Lo que hizo
	ir a la joyería a comprar _____
	ir a la zapatería a comprar _____
	ir a la librería a comprar _____

¡Festejemos!

SITUATION You and your partner are discussing how you spent different holidays last year.

TASK 1 Ask your partner where he or she spent the following holidays. Then ask if he or she did each activity listed in the chart below. Complete the chart according to your partner's responses.

MODELO A — ¿Dónde pasaron la Navidad el año pasado?
B — La pasamos en casa de mis abuelos.
A — ¿Recibiste muchos regalos?
B — Sí, recibí muchos regalos. Y también comí con la familia.

Día festivo	Lo pasaron...	Actividades	Sí/No
la Navidad	en casa de sus abuelos	recibió muchos regalos comió con la familia	Sí
el Día de Acción de Gracias		comer una cena muy rica _____	
la Nochevieja		ver fuegos artificiales _____	
el Día de la Madre		comer en un restaurante _____	
la Nochebuena		ir a misa a medianoche _____	

TASK 2 Now, answer your partner's questions about where and how you spent the following holidays. Then, tell your partner about one more activity you did for each holiday.

Día festivo	Lo pasamos...	Actividades
el Día de los Enamorados	en el salón de clase	recibir tarjetas yo/decorar el salón de clase
el Año Nuevo	en casa de mis tíos	no ver fuegos artificiales yo/reunirse con la familia
el Hanukah	en casa	ir a la sinagoga mi prima y yo/recibir regalos
el Día de la Independencia	en el parque	no ir a la playa yo/asistir a una fiesta

¡Festejemos!

SITUATION You and your partner are discussing how you spent different holidays last year.

TASK 1 Answer your partner's questions about where and how you spent the following holidays. Then tell your partner about one more activity you did for each holiday.

MODELO A — ¿Dónde pasaron la Navidad el año pasado?
B — La pasamos en casa de mis abuelos.
A — ¿Recibiste muchos regalos?
B — Sí, recibí muchos regalos. Y también comí con la familia.

Día festivo	Lo pasamos...	Actividades
la Navidad	en casa de mis abuelos	recibir muchos regalos yo/comer con la familia
el Día de Acción de Gracias	en casa de mis tíos	comer una cena muy rica yo/invitar a unos amigos
la Nochevieja	en casa de mis abuelos	ver fuegos artificiales nosotros/hacer una fiesta
el Día de la Madre	en casa	no comer en un restaurante mi madre/recibir tarjetas
la Nochebuena	en la iglesia	no ir a misa a medianoche nosotros/reunirse con la familia

TASK 2 Now, ask your partner where he or she spent the following holidays. Then ask if he or she did each activity listed in the chart below. Complete the chart according to your partner's responses.

Día festivo	Lo pasaron...	Actividades	Sí/No
el Día de los Enamorados		recibir tarjetas _____	
el Año Nuevo		ver fuegos artificiales _____	
el Hanukah		ir a la sinagoga _____	
el Día de la Independencia		ir a la playa _____	

34

¡Festejemos!

SITUATION You are the owner of a catering company and your partner is your assistant. You are catering a wedding and surprise party tomorrow but everything isn't ready!

TASK 1 In order to speed things up, you have changed the original task list for the wedding. Ask your partner if the following people have already done their duties. Take note of what has been done and what is being done.

MODELO A —¿Ya compraste las flores?
   B — Sí, las compré anoche.
   A — ¿Ya decoraste el pastel de boda?
   B — No. Patrick está decorándolo ahora.
      or Patrick lo está decorando ahora.

La boda de las familias Escamilla y Muñoz	
Quehaceres	**Quién los hizo o está haciendo**
your partner: comprar las flores	Las compró anoche.
your partner: decorar el pastel de boda	Patrick está decorándolo ahora.
your partner: lavar los platos	
Luis: preparar el ponche	
Isabel: comprar las galletas	
Roberto: colgar las decoraciones	
Antonio: llamar a los invitados	
Alfredo: mandar las invitaciones	

TASK 2 Now, switch roles. To speed things along you have reassigned some tasks to employees not previously working on the wedding. Answer your partner's questions according to the chart. If a task has been reassigned, it is being done right now.

La fiesta sorpresa de Laia Banderas	
Quehaceres	**Quién los hizo o está haciendo**
preparar el ponche	tú/ahora
colgar la piñata	Anita/anoche
cortar el pastel de chocolate	Pablo/ahora
comprar los CDs	Clara/anteayer
decorar la casa	Arturo/ahora
comprar los dulces	Rosa/ayer

35

¡Festejemos!

COMMUNICATIVE ACTIVITY 2B

SITUATION Your partner is the owner of a catering company and you are his or her assistant. You are catering a wedding and surprise party tomorrow but everything isn't ready!

TASK 1 In order to speed things up, your partner has changed the original task list for the wedding. Answer your partner about whether the following people have already done their duties. Say what has been done and what is being done.

MODELO A —¿Ya compraste las flores?
   B — Sí, las compré anoche.
   A — ¿Ya decoraste el pastel de boda?
   B — No. Patrick está decorándolo ahora.
      or Patrick lo está decorando ahora.

La boda de las familias Escamilla y Muñoz	
Quehaceres	**Quién los hizo o está haciendo**
comprar las flores anoche	tú/anoche
decorar el pastel de boda	Patrick/ahora
lavar los platos	Roberto/ahora
preparar el ponche	Patricio/anteayer
comprar las galletas	Paquita/ahora
colgar las decoraciones	Isabel/anoche
llamar a los invitados	Sara/ahora
mandar las invitaciones	Antonio/la semana pasada

TASK 2 Now, switch roles. In order to speed things up, your partner has changed the original task list for the surprise party. Ask your partner if the following people have already done their tasks. Take notes on what has been done and what is being done.

La fiesta sorpresa de Laia Banderas	
Quehaceres	**Quién los hizo o está haciendo**
your partner: preparar el ponche	
your partner: colgar la piñata	
Clara: cortar el pastel de chocolate	
Paco: comprar los CDs	
Rosa: decorar la casa	
Daniel: comprar los dulces	

      36

¡A viajar!

SITUATION You and your partner are about to take your first international flight and you are both very nervous. You are trying to help each other remember everything that needs to be done.

TASK 1 Ask your partner if he or she has done the following things. Write in your notebook all of his or her responses.

MODELO   A — ¿Ya hiciste todas las maletas?
         B — Sí, hice todas las maletas. *or* Sí, las hice.
         A — ¿Pasaste por la oficina de cambio?
         B — ¡Ay, no! Todavía no. Debo pasar por la oficina de cambio. *or*
             ¡Ay, no! Todavía tengo que pasar por la oficina de cambio.

Cosas por hacer	¿Ya las hizo?
hacer todas las maletas	Sí, ...
pasar por la oficina de cambio	No, ...
encontrar el pasaporte	
pasar por el cajero automático	
pagar el boleto	
encontrarse con tus amigos	
conseguir un mapa	
hablar con la agente	

TASK 2 Now, switch roles. Answer your partner's questions about what you have and have not done for your trip. If there is something that you haven't done, say that you need to do it. Use direct object pronouns when possible.

Sí	No
hacer cola delante del mostrador	ver en la pantalla la puerta del vuelo
sacar dinero	comprar revistas para el viaje
buscar a mis amigos	pasar por la aduana

¡A viajar!

SITUATION You and your partner are about to take your first international flight and you are both very nervous. You are trying to help each other remember everything that needs to be done.

TASK 1 Answer your partner's questions about what you have and have not done for your trip. If there is something that you haven't done, say that you need to do it. Use direct object pronouns when possible.

MODELO A — ¿Ya hiciste todas las maletas?

B — Sí, hice todas las maletas. *or* Sí, las hice.

A — ¿Pasaste por la oficina de cambio?

B — ¡Ay, no! Todavía no. Debo pasar por la oficina de cambio. *or*

¡Ay, no! Todavía tengo que pasar por la oficina de cambio.

Sí	No
hacer todas las maletas	pasar por la oficina de cambio
encontrar el pasaporte	pasar por el cajero automático
pagar el boleto	encontrarme con mis amigos
hablar con la agente	conseguir un mapa

TASK 2 Now, switch roles. Ask your partner if he or she has done the following things. Write in your notebook all of his or her responses.

Cosas por hacer	¿Ya las hizo?
hacer cola delante del mostrador	
ver en la pantalla la puerta del vuelo	
sacar dinero	
comprar revistas para el viaje	
pasar por la aduana	
buscar a tus amigos	

¡A viajar!

SITUATION You and your partner are planning this year's vacations but are having trouble thinking of places to go.

TASK 1 You have many ideas of what to do on vacation, but you just don't know where to go. Tell your partner about your ideas. Then, answer his or her questions. He or she will recommend a destination for you.

MODELO A — Pienso viajar este verano.
B — ¿Adónde quieres ir?
A — No sé. Me gustaría ir a la playa.
B — ¿Qué te gustaría hacer?
A — Me gustaría/quiero tomar el sol, ir de pesca y ver una isla.
B — Pues, viaja a Miami, Florida.

la estación	el verano	el otoño	el invierno
¿Adónde?			
Cosas por hacer	tomar el sol, ir de pesca, ver una isla	acampar, ir a las montañas, ir de excursión	sacar fotos, visitar los museos, tomar el metro, ir de compras
Destino	Miami, Florida		

TASK 2 Now, switch roles. Listen to your partner's ideas of when he or she plans to vacation. Ask your partner where he or she wants to go and what he or she would like to do. Take notes. Based on his or her response, choose the destination that best suits his or her wishes.

la estación		
¿Adónde?		
Cosas por hacer		
Destino		

Destinos

Buenos Aires, Argentina

San José, Costa Rica

¡A viajar!

SITUATION You and your partner are planning this year's vacations but are having trouble thinking of places to go.

TASK 1 Listen to your partner's ideas of when he or she plans to vacation this year. Ask your partner where he or she wants to go and what he or she would like to do. Take notes. Based on his or her response, choose the destination that best suits his or her wishes.

MODELO A — Pienso viajar este verano.
B — ¿Adónde quieres ir?
A — No sé. Me gustaría ir a la playa.
B — ¿Qué te gustaría hacer?
A — Me gustaría/quiero tomar el sol, ir de pesca y ver una isla.
B — Pues, viaja a Miami, Florida.

la estación	el verano		
¿Adónde?			
Cosas por hacer	tomar el sol, ir de pesca, ver una isla		
Destino	Miami, Florida		

Destinos

Miami, Florida

Madrid, España

un parque nacional, Texas

TASK 2 Now, switch roles. You have many ideas of what to do this summer and spring, you just don't know where to go. Tell your partner about your ideas. Then, answer his or her questions. He or she will recommend a destination for you.

la estación	el verano	la primavera
¿Adónde?		
Cosas por hacer	subir a las montañas, sacar fotos de los volcanes	pasear en bote de vela, esquiar en el agua, bailar tango, ver el Océano Atlántico
Destino		

40

Holt Spanish 1

Picture Sequences

¡Empecemos!

Today is the first day of class for a new exchange student. In groups of three, create a conversation based on what you see in each scene below.

(43)

A conocernos

Juan and Perla are trying to decide what to do on their date. Using the pictures, work with a partner to describe what Juan and Perla like and dislike.

¿Qué te gusta hacer?

Two friends decide on what to do for the weekend. With a partner, create a conversation based on what you see in each scene below.

La vida escolar

Two classmates talk to each other throughout the school day. With a partner, create a conversation based on what you see in each scene below.

En casa con la familia

Two friends describe their lives at home. With a partner, create a conversation based on what you see in each scene below.

¡A comer!

Today is a typical day for the Galván family. With a partner, create a conversation
based on what you see in each scene below.

Cuerpo sano, mente sana

A girl struggles through a school day with her best friend. With a partner, create a conversation based on what you see in each scene below.

Vamos de compras

Two friends discuss their shopping experiences with one another. With a partner, create a conversation based on what you see in each scene below.

¡Festejemos!

Today is the 20th wedding anniversary of Susana Felipe's parents. With a partner, create a conversation based on what you see in each scene below.

¡A viajar!

Mrs. Trujillo drops her daughter off at the airport and picks her up at the end of her trip. With a partner, create a conversation based on what you see in each scene below.

Holt Spanish 1

Interpersonal Communication Cards

¡Empecemos!

INTERPERSONAL COMMUNICATION: INTERVIEWS

Vocabulario 1/Gramática 1

You are showing me a photo of two of your friends. I would like to know more about them. Respond to my questions.

Hola, ¿cómo estás?

¿Quién es el muchacho?

¿De dónde es él?

¿Cómo se llama la muchacha?

Vocabulario 2/Gramática 2

You would like to participate in an exchange program with Spain next year. Answer my questions so that I can send you some information and note the date and time of your request.

¿Cómo te llamas?

¿Cómo se escribe *(name)*?

¿Cuál es tu teléfono?

¿Qué fecha es hoy?

¿Qué hora es?

Repaso

I am the class president and am greeting you, a new student. I want to ask you a few questions to later show you around and help you meet new people. Respond to my questions.

Hola, ¿cómo te llamas?

¿Cómo se escribe *(name)*?

¿De dónde eres?

¿Cuál es tu correo electrónico?

¿Cuál es tu teléfono?

¡Empecemos!

INTERPERSONAL COMMUNICATION: ROLE-PLAYS

Vocabulario 1/Gramática 1

STUDENT A Imagine that you are meeting **Student B** on the first day of school. Greet **Student B,** ask his or her name, how he or she is, and where he or she is from. Respond to **Student B** when he or she says good-bye.

STUDENT B Imagine that today is the first day at school and **Student A** starts to talk to you. Respond to **Student A**'s greeting and questions. Then tell **Student A** you are pleased to meet him or her, and say good-bye.

Vocabulario 2/Gramática 2

STUDENT A Imagine that you are very absent-minded and need help remembering the information for the heading of a class assignment. Ask **Student B** to spell your teacher's name and to give you the day, date, and time. Remember to thank **Student B.**

STUDENT B Imagine that **Student A** is very absent-minded. Answer **Student A**'s questions about the information he or she needs for the heading of a class assignment.

Repaso

STUDENT A You and **Student B** are exchanging contact information. Ask for **Student B**'s name, where he or she is from, and his or her e-mail address and telephone number. Ask **Student B** to spell out his or her e-mail address. Then answer **Student B**'s questions.

STUDENT B You and **Student A** are exchanging contact information. Answer **Student A**'s questions. Then ask **Student A** for his or her name, where he or she is from, and his or her e-mail address and telephone number. Ask **Student A** to spell out his or her e-mail address.

A conocernos

INTERPERSONAL COMMUNICATION: INTERVIEWS

Vocabulario 1/Gramática 1

You spotted me during our lunch break, and covered my eyes from behind my back.
I am asking you some questions to guess your identity. Respond to my questions.

¿Cómo eres?

¿Eres rubio(a)?

¿Cuántos años tienes?

¿Eres alto(a) o bajo(a)?

¿Quién es tu mejor amigo(a)?

Vocabulario 2/Gramática 2

I am new to the class and am eager to know more about my new school and my classmates. How would you answer my questions?

¿Cómo es la clase de historia?

¿Te gustan las ciencias? ¿Por qué (no)?

¿A quién no le gustan las ciencias?

¿Te gusta más la clase de arte o la clase de álgebra?

Repaso

I am a sports fan and am asking you a few questions to see if you share similar interests with me. Respond to my questions.

¿Eres atlético(a)?

¿Te gustan los deportes?

¿Por qué (no) te gustan los deportes?

¿Eres activo(a)?

¿Te gustan los videojuegos de deportes?

A conocernos

INTERPERSONAL COMMUNICATION: ROLE-PLAYS

Vocabulario 1/Gramática 1

STUDENT A You and **Student B** are describing your best friends. Ask **Student B** to describe his or her best friend. Then answer **Student B**'s questions.

STUDENT B You and **Student A** are describing your best friends. Answer **Student A**'s questions. Then ask **Student A** to describe his or her best friend.

Vocabulario 2/Gramática 2

STUDENT A You and **Student B** are talking about books. First ask **Student B** whether he or she likes adventure books, and then ask if he or she likes romantic books. Ask **Student B** which of these two types he or she likes best. Then answer the questions **Student B** asks you.

STUDENT B You and **Student A** are talking about books. Answer **Student A**'s questions. After answering them, ask **Student A** whether he or she likes science fiction books, and then ask if he or she likes mystery books. Then ask **Student A** which of these two types he or she likes best.

Repaso

STUDENT A You and **Student B** have just been introduced. Ask **Student B** to describe himself or herself and say how old he or she is. Ask **Student B** about his or her likes and dislikes. Then answer the questions that **Student B** asks you.

STUDENT B You and **Student A** have just been introduced. Answer **Student A**'s questions. Then ask **Student A** to describe himself or herself and say how old he or she is. Ask **Student A** about his or her likes and dislikes.

¿Qué te gusta hacer?

INTERPERSONAL COMMUNICATION: INTERVIEWS

Vocabulario 1/Gramática 1

I am a new student at your school and would like to get to know you and your friends better. Respond to my questions.

¿Qué te gusta hacer?

¿Qué le gusta hacer a tu mejor amigo(a)?

¿Qué les gusta hacer a ti y a tus amigos(as)?

¿Te gusta jugar a los deportes?

¿Quieres jugar al tenis conmigo?

Vocabulario 2/Gramática 2

I am a reporter writing a story on what teenagers in the United States do in their free time. I am interviewing everyone in your class. Respond to my questions.

¿Adónde vas los fines de semana?

¿Qué haces con tus amigos los sábados?

¿Con qué frecuencia vas a la piscina?

¿Qué haces cuando hace buen tiempo?

¿Adónde vas cuando llueve?

Repaso

I would like to invite your best friend to do something this weekend but don't know him or her very well. Answer my questions so that I have a better idea of what to ask your friend to do.

¿Qué le gusta hacer a tu mejor amigo(a)?

¿Le gusta jugar a los deportes?

¿Adónde va los sábados?

¿Qué hace él (ella) cuando hace buen tiempo?

¿Quieres salir con nosotros?

¿Qué te gusta hacer?

INTERPERSONAL COMMUNICATION: ROLE-PLAYS

Vocabulario 1/Gramática 1

STUDENT A **Student B** is explaining what he or she likes to do with friends. You misunderstand some of what is said. Ask **Student B** to clarify who likes to do the following activities: to draw, to play soccer, to go to the movies. Then, answer **Student B**'s questions about your friends.

STUDENT B **Student A** misunderstands some of what you say about what you and your friends like to do. Answer **Student A**'s questions. Then, ask **Student A** which of his or her friends likes to do the following activities: to skate, to go shopping, to write letters.

Vocabulario 2/Gramática 2

STUDENT A You and **Student B** are discussing what you do and where you go on weekends. Ask **Student B** what he or she does and where he or she goes on Saturdays. Also, ask what **Student B** does when the weather is bad. Respond to **Student B**'s questions.

STUDENT B You and **Student B** are discussing what you do and where you go on weekends. Answer **Student A**'s questions and then ask what he or she does and where he or she likes to go on Sundays. Also ask what **Student A** does when the weather is nice.

Repaso

STUDENT A It is raining on a Saturday afternoon and you and **Student B** are trying to think of things to do. Ask **Student B** if he or she likes to do the following: to surf the Web, to draw, to go to the movies. Then, ask **Student B** if he or she wants to do those things with you.

STUDENT B It is raining on a Saturday afternoon and you and **Student A** are trying to think of things to do. Answer **Student A**'s questions. Then, ask **Student A** if he or she likes to do the following things: to go to the gym, to rent videos, to listen to music. Also ask **Student A** if he or she wants to do those things with you.

La vida escolar

INTERPERSONAL COMMUNICATION: INTERVIEWS

Vocabulario 1/Gramática 1

I am a friend of yours visiting from Costa Rica and I am interested in knowing what school life is like for you. Answer my questions.

¿A qué hora vienes al colegio?

¿Qué clases tienes por la mañana y por la tarde?

¿Necesitas algo para el colegio?

¿Cuál es tu materia preferida?

¿Es fácil o difícil?

Vocabulario 2/Gramática 2

I am a classmate of yours and would like to make plans with you. Respond to my questions and invitations. Tell me why you can or can't come with me to certain events.

¿Qué vas a hacer la próxima semana?

¿Qué vas a hacer el lunes próximo por la tarde?

¿A qué hora vas a llegar al partido de fútbol pasado mañana?

Hay una reunión del club de francés el viernes próximo. Vas a ir conmigo, ¿no?

¿Vienes conmigo a la biblioteca el domingo próximo después del almuerzo?

Repaso

I am the president of the Spanish Club and am planning future events. Repond to my questionnaire.

¿Qúe clase tienes primero los martes?

¿Qué vas a hacer el jueves próximo por la tarde?

¿Cuánta tarea tienes la próxima semana?

¿Tienes ganas de tener una fiesta del club de español?

¿Qué tal si tenemos una reunión la próxima semana?

CAPÍTULO

4

La vida escolar

INTERPERSONAL COMMUNICATION: ROLE-PLAYS

Vocabulario 1/Gramática 1

STUDENT A Imagine that you are **Student B**'s parent and today was his or her first day of school. Ask **Student B** what classes he or she has in the morning and after lunch. Also, ask which subject is his or her favorite, and why. Finally, ask **Student B** if he or she needs a lot of school supplies, and if so, how many of each.

STUDENT B **Student A** is your parent and today was your first day of school. Answer **Student A**'s questions about the following schedule: math, German, history, computer science, workshop, biology, and chemistry.

Vocabulario 2/Gramática 2

STUDENT A You invite **Student B** to go with you to a few school events next week. Invite **Student B** to each event and then answer his or her questions.

STUDENT B **Student A** is inviting you to do something with him or her next week. He or she invites you to a few events, but you are too busy. Ask **Student A** what time each event starts. Then, decline the invitation telling **Student A** that you have to do certain things. Use these phrases in your answers.

Hay un(a)...   **por la mañana**   **por la tarde**   **el martes próximo**   **Tengo que...**

Repaso

STUDENT A There is an event after math class next Tuesday that many students are going to. You think **Student B** is going, but you aren't sure. Remind **Student B** of the event and ask if he or she is going to go. Then, answer **Student B**'s questions.

STUDENT B **Student A** reminds you of an event that is happening next Tuesday. Tell **Student A** that you can't go because you have to buy certain school supplies. Ask if **Student A** needs any school supplies. If he or she does, invite **Student A** to come with you.

62

En casa con la familia

CAPÍTULO

5

INTERPERSONAL COMMUNICATION: INTERVIEWS

Vocabulario 1/Gramática 1

I am the town historian and am recording the demographics of the families who live in town. Respond to my questions.

¿Cuántas personas hay en tu familia?

¿Cómo son tus padres?

¿A qué hora empiezan a trabajar tus padres?

¿Cuántas personas usan lentes?

¿Cuántas horas duermen ustedes?

Vocabulario 2/Gramática 2

Imagine that your family is having a party and I'm calling to get directions to your house. How would you respond to my questions?

¿Dónde viven ustedes?

¿Cuál es tu dirección?

¿Cómo es tu casa?

¿Está en la ciudad, las afueras o el campo?

¿Te parece fácil encontrar tu casa?

Repaso

I am a technician who is repairing something in your house. Answer my questions so that I can find your house, recognize your family, and better serve you.

¿Dónde está tu casa?

¿Está al lado de una calle muy grande?

¿Cuál es tu dirección?

¿Cómo son sus padres y hermanos?

¿Hasta qué hora duermen ustedes los fines de semana?

CAPÍTULO

En casa con la familia

5

INTERPERSONAL COMMUNICATION: ROLE-PLAYS

Vocabulario 1/Gramática 1

STUDENT A You and **Student B** are talking about your families, real or imaginary. Ask **Student B** how many people are in his or her family. Also, find out what his or her family members are like. Ask **Student B** at what time his or her family eats lunch on weekends. Then, answer **Student B**'s questions.

STUDENT B You and **Student B** are talking about your families, real or imaginary. Answer **Student A**'s questions and then ask if his or her family is small or large. Also, ask **Student A** what his or her family members are like. Ask how many people have blonde hair.

Vocabulario 2/Gramática 2

STUDENT A You and **Student B** are imagining that you each live in your dream home. Ask **Student B** about his or her dream home. Where does **Student B** live? What is his or her apartment or house like? Is **Student B**'s home near school? Answer **Student B**'s questions.

STUDENT B You and **Student A** are imagining that you each live in your dream home. Answer **Student A**'s questions about your dream home. Then, ask **Student A** who does the chores in this dream home. Also, ask **Student A** what he or she specifically has to do.

Repaso

STUDENT A Imagine that you and **Student B** both have family members that don't do chores. Tell **Student B** that your brother, sister, and grandfather never have to do the following chores: clean the living room, take out the trash, and cut the grass. Listen to **Student B**'s remarks and answer his or her questions.

STUDENT B Imagine that you and **Student A** both have family members that don't do chores. **Student A** tells you about his or her family members that don't do chores. After each of his or her statements, tell **Student A** that your grandmother, father, and brother don't do those chores either. After **Student A** finishes his or her statements, ask him or her what he or she thinks about this situation.

Holt Spanish 1

Activities for Communication

CAPÍTULO

¡A comer!

6

INTERPERSONAL COMMUNICATION: INTERVIEWS

Vocabulario 1/Gramática 1

I am an exchange student from Mexico and am interested in what you and your friends like to eat. Respond to my questions.

¿Qué prefieres pedir para el almuerzo?

¿Qué prefieres pedir para comer y beber en un restaurante?

¿Qué comida sirven en tu colegio y cómo está?

¿Qué sirven de cena en casa los fines de semana?

Vocabulario 2/Gramática 2

I am a friend that has come over to help you prepare for a large family dinner. Answer my questions by using informal commands and direct object pronouns when possible.

¿Qué vamos a cenar esta noche?

¿Quién va a preparar la cena?

¿Necesitas ayuda con la cena? ¿Puedo ayudar?

¿Pruebo la ensalada de atún antes de ponerla en la mesa?

¿Cómo caliento la carne?

Repaso

You are taking me to a restaurant that I've never been to. Answer my questions and use direct object pronouns when possible.

¿Aquí preparan el pescado muy bien?

¿Qué prefieres, la carne o el pescado?

¿Cuál postre prefieres tú? ¿Por qué?

¿Sirven muchos sándwiches?

¿Qué vas a almorzar?

65

¡A comer!

INTERPERSONAL COMMUNICATION: ROLE-PLAYS

Vocabulario 1/Gramática 1

STUDENT A Imagine that you're a server in a resturante and **Student B** is your customer. Ask **Student B** what he or she would like to order. Listen to **Student B**'s answer. Then, suggest a few lunch items and tell what they are like at your restaurant. After **Student B** orders his or her main course, ask **Student B** if he or she would like anything else.

STUDENT B Imagine that your server (**Student A**) has just come up to you to take your order. When he or she asks what you would like, tell **Student A** that you don't know. Listen to **Student A** describe a few menu items. Then, tell **Student A** what you would like and answer his or her last questions.

¿Qué tal si prueba...? Yo quisiera... riquísimo(a) (muy) bien bueno(a)

Vocabulario 2/Gramática 2

STUDENT A You and **Student B** are having breakfast at your house. Ask **Student B** if he or she eats bacon, eggs, and toast for breakfast. Then ask if **Student B** drinks milk in the morning. Now, listen to **Student B**'s questions and respond by telling him or her what to do in order to prepare breakfast.

STUDENT B You are at **Student A**'s house for breakfast. Answer **Student A**'s questions about what you eat. Then ask him or her who is going to prepare breakfast. Also ask if you can help.

Repaso

STUDENT A You are in a restaurant recommending meals to **Student B**. Ask **Student B** why he or she doesn't try the chicken with rice, the tuna salad, or the cheese sandwich. Describe each of those dishes to **Student B**. Listen to **Student B**'s reply, then tell him or her to order the tomato soup or the fish. They are very good.

STUDENT B **Student A** is recommending food to you in a restaurant. Listen to his or her first three suggestions and say that you don't want to order any of those dishes. Then listen to **Student A**'s next suggestion and say that you prefer the fish to the tomato soup.

Cuerpo sano, mente sana

INTERPERSONAL COMMUNICATION: INTERVIEWS

Vocabulario 1/Gramática 1

I am out of shape and often late to school. You, on the other hand, are in shape and punctual. Answer my questions so that I will have a better idea of how to improve my daily routine and work out more often.

¿Cómo te mantienes en forma?

¿Qué haces antes de entrenarte?

¿Qué haces todos los días para relajarte?

¿Cuándo prefieres bañarte?

¿Qué tienes que hacer para llegar a la escuela a tiempo?

Vocabulario 2/Gramática 2

You are the host of a radio advice show. I am calling in to ask for your help. Answer my questions.

Casi siempre me siento cansado. ¿Qué debo hacer para cuidarme mejor?

Como demasiado dulce y grasa. ¿Qué debo hacer?

Me duelen los pies. ¿Qué debo hacer?

Tengo catarro. ¿Qué debo hacer para cuidarme mejor?

Siempre estoy nervioso. ¿Qué debo hacer?

Repaso

I am conducting a class survey on students' overall health habits. Respond to my questions.

¿Cómo te sientes después de entrenarte?

¿Qué haces todos los días para relajarte?

¿Duermes lo suficiente? ¿Cuántas horas duermes?

¿Sigues una dieta sana? ¿Qué comes?

Cuando tienes catarro, ¿qué haces para cuidarte?

CAPÍTULO

7

Cuerpo sano, mente sana

INTERPERSONAL COMMUNICATION: ROLE-PLAYS

Vocabulario 1/Gramática 1

STUDENT A You and **Student B** are going to the movies, but he or she is running late. Ask **Student B** if he or she is ready. Then, ask what he or she still has to do. Listen to **Student B**'s anwers and then switch roles. Tell **Student B** that you aren't ready. Then, give him or her reasons why you aren't.

STUDENT B You and **Student A** are going to the movies, but you are running late. Respond to **Student A**'s questions. Tell him or her that you just got dressed and that you have to dry your hair before you eat lunch. Now, switch roles. Ask **Student A** if he or she is ready. Then, ask what he or she has to do. Use these phrases in your conversation.

  lavarse la cara   peinarse el pelo   secarse el pelo   bañarse   antes de

Vocabulario 2/Gramática 2

STUDENT A You and **Student B** both aren't feeling well. Tell **Student B** that he or she doesn't look well. Listen to **Student B**'s response, then ask if he or she has a cold. After **Student B** responds, tell him or her to take care and to drink orange juice. Now, listen to **Student B**'s question. Tell him or her that your stomach hurts.

STUDENT B You and **Student A** both aren't feeling well. Listen to **Student A**'s question and tell him or her that your head hurts and that you are tired. When **Student A** asks if you have a cold, say yes. Ask **Student A** what's wrong with him or her. Listen to his or her answer. Tell **Student A** that he or she shouldn't eat so many sweets.

Repaso

STUDENT A You and **Student B** are talking about his or her daily routine. You realize that he or she has some unhealthy habits. Ask **Student B** what he or she does to relax. Listen to his or her answer. Then, ask **Student B** how he or she stays in shape. After **Student B** answers, give him or her advice on how to take better care.

STUDENT B You are telling **Student A** about your daily routine. Listen to **Student A**'s question. Respond by saying that you watch T.V. and sleep to relax. Then, listen to **Student A**'s question and answer by saying that you don't stay in shape. Listen to his or her advice.

Vamos de compras

INTERPERSONAL COMMUNICATION: INTERVIEWS

Vocabulario 1/Gramática 1

Imagine that you and your family recently moved from a cold-weather state to Miami. I am a friend from your home town. Answer my questions.

¿Cuánto cuestan los pantalones vaqueros en tu tienda preferida?

¿Qué llevas cuándo hace frío?

¿Qué llevas para ir a la playa?

¿Son tan caras las sandalias como las botas?

¿Prefieres calcetines de lana o de algodón? ¿Por qué?

Vocabulario 2/Gramática 2

I am your mother and I just came back from a week-long business trip. You are eager to tell me about your shopping experience last weekend. Answer my questions.

¿Qué hiciste el fin de semana pasado?

¿Con quién fuiste?

¿Qué compraste?

¿Dónde encontraste una camisa tan bonita como ésta?

¿Qué almorzaste en la plaza de comidas?

Repaso

Imagine that you won a shopping spree in Little Havana last weekend. I am a friend interested in hearing all of the details. Answer my questions.

¿Adónde fuiste de compras el viernes pasado?

¿Dónde compraste estas botas rojas?

¿Cuánto dinero gastaste en la joyería?

¿Cuánto costó todo lo que compraste?

¿Son las otras tiendas de Miami más caras que las tiendas de aquí?

CAPÍTULO

8

Vamos de compras

INTERPERSONAL COMMUNICATION: ROLE-PLAYS

Vocabulario 1/Gramática 1

STUDENT A   Imagine that you work in a clothing store and **Student B** is your client. Ask **Student B** how you can help him or her. **Student B** asks you how much several items cost. When telling the price, repeat the name of each item. Then, ask **Student B** how each item fits.

STUDENT B   You are shopping in a clothing store and **Student A** (a clerk) asks if you need help. Ask how much the following items cost: this silk shirt, those black shoes, that red T-shirt, that wool sweater. **Student A** asks you how each of these items fits. Respond to him or her.

Vocabulario 2/Gramática 2

STUDENT A   You call **Student B** on the phone. Respond to **Student B**'s greeting. Ask **Student B** what he or she did yesterday. Listen to **Student B**'s answer. Then ask **Student B** to tell you the stores he or she went to and what he or she bought in each one.

STUDENT B   **Student A** calls your house and you answer the phone. Greet **Student A.** Listen to his or her question and respond by saying that you went to the mall yesterday. Then, respond to **Student A** by naming each of the stores you went to and saying what you bought in each one.

Repaso

STUDENT A   You and **Student B** went shopping, but not with each other. You bought boots, a sweater, and socks, but in different colors or materials. Answer **Student B**'s questions. Then ask **Student B** how much his or her items cost. After he or she answers, compare items.

STUDENT B   You and **Student A** went shopping, but not with each other. You bought boots, a sweater, and socks, but in different colors or materials. Ask **Student A** where he or she bought his or her items. Then answer his or her questions. Compare items.

¡Festejemos!

INTERPERSONAL COMMUNICATION: INTERVIEWS

Vocabulario 1/Gramática 1

You and I are discussing the holidays. Respond to my questions about how you celebrated last year and your plans for this year.

¿Cuál es tu día festivo preferido? ¿Por qué?

¿Dónde pasaron el Año Nuevo el año pasado?

¿Cómo festejaste el Día de la Madre el año pasado?

¿Qué piensas hacer para celebrar el Día de la Independencia?

¿Adónde vas a ir el Día de los Enamorados?

Vocabulario 2/Gramática 2

I am a friend who has just come over to your house to help prepare for a surprise birthday party. Answer my questions in complete sentences using direct object pronouns when possible.

¿Ya mandaste las invitaciones a todos los invitados?

¿Qué estás haciendo ahora?

¿Quién está preparando el ponche?

¿Dónde debo poner los dulces y las galletas?

¿Me necesitas para algo más?

Repaso

I heard from a friend that you had a great party last weekend. I'm interested in hearing all about it. Respond to my questions.

¿Qué ocasión especial festejaron?

¿Qué tal estuvo la fiesta?

¿Qué pasó en la fiesta?

¿Qué prepararon de comida? ¿Quién la preparó?

¿Qué planes tienes para tu próxima fiesta?

¡Festejemos!

INTERPERSONAL COMMUNICATION: ROLE-PLAYS

Vocabulario 1/Gramática 1

STUDENT A   You and **Student B** are discussing upcoming holidays. Ask **Student B** what he or she is doing on New Year's Eve and Valentine's Day. Listen to **Student B**'s responses. Then, answer **Student B**'s questions by saying what you plan to do for certain holidays.

STUDENT B   You and **Student A** are discussing upcoming holidays. Listen to **Student A**'s questions. Then answer **Student A**'s questions by telling him or her what you plan to do for certain holidays. After answering all of **Student A**'s questions, ask **Student A** what he or she plans to do for Independence Day and Father's Day.

Vocabulario 2/Gramática 2

STUDENT A   You and your cousin meet **Student B** (a friend you haven't seen in a while). Greet **Student B**. Listen to him or her, then ask if he or she knows your cousin Leslie. After **Student B** replies, introduce your cousin to **Student B**. Listen to **Student B,** then say goodbye.

STUDENT B   **Student A** is a friend that you haven't seen in a while. Listen to **Student A**, then greet him or her. Listen to **Student A** and say that you do not know his or her cousin. After being presented to **Student A**'s cousin, tell Leslie that it is nice to meet her. Say goodbye to Leslie and **Student A.**

Repaso

STUDENT A   **Student B** had a New Year's party last year. Ask if he or she did the following to prepare for the party: bought flowers, prepared punch, hung decorations. After **Student B** responds, answer his or her questions. Say that you went to your grandparent's house. Listen to **Student B** and explain what you did last New Year's Eve.

STUDENT B   You had a New Year's party last year. Respond to **Student A**'s questions by saying that you did all of those things. Now, ask **Student A** how he or she spent last New Year's. Listen to his or her response. Then ask how staying with his or her grandparents was.

(72)

¡A viajar!

INTERPERSONAL COMMUNICATION: INTERVIEWS

Vocabulario 1/Gramática 1

You just got back from vacation and we are talking about your trip. Answer my questions.

¿A qué hora comenzaste tu viaje?

¿Cambiaste dinero antes o después de llegar al aueropuerto?

¿Trajiste todas tus cosas o dejaste algo importante en casa?

¿Cuánto tiempo hiciste cola delante del mostrador?

¿Cómo fue tu vuelo? ¿Qué hiciste cuando llegaste?

Vocabulario 2/Gramática 2

You and I are discussing last year's summer vacations. Imagine that you traveled to a big city. Answer my questions.

¿Adónde fuiste de vacaciones el verano pasado?

¿Qué tal el viaje?

¿Qué hicieron tu familia y tú allí en _____?

¿Qué lugares de interés recorrieron?

¿Adónde piensas ir en tu próximo viaje? ¿Por qúe?

Repaso

Imagine that I am one of your parents and we are waiting in a long line to board a plane to Lima, Perú. Respond to my questions

¿Qué esperas hacer en Lima?

¿Me puedes decir a qué hora vamos a llegar?

¿Te gustaría quedarte en casa de los abuelos o en un hotel?

¡Ay no! ¿Dónde dejaste tu carnet de identidad?

¿Qué tenemos que hacer en el aeropuerto de Lima?

(73)

¡A viajar!

INTERPERSONAL COMMUNICATION: ROLE-PLAYS

Vocabulario 1/Gramática 1

STUDENT A   You have never been to an airport before today. Ask **Student B** where you can board the plane, buy an airplane ticket, and claim luggage. Listen to **Student B**'s responses. Switch roles. Answer **Student B** by saying that you don't know, or that what he or she is looking for is around the corner.

STUDENT B   Today is **Student A**'s first time in an airport. Answer **Student A**'s questions. Switch roles. Ask **Student A** if he or she can tell you where the bathrooms, the money exchange, and the ticket counter are. Listen to his or her responses.

Vocabulario 2/Gramática 2

STUDENT A   You and **Student B** have different ideas about your vacation. Tell **Student B** that you would first like to go out in a canoe. Then you want to go fishing. Later, you hope to water ski. Listen to **Student B**'s comments after each of your statements.

STUDENT B   You and **Student A** have different ideas about your vacation. Listen to **Student A**. After each of his or her statements, give a negative, and then an affirmative command.

Primero...   Luego...   Después...   ¡No hagas...!   Haz...   ¡No vayas...!   Ve...

Repaso

STUDENT A   You and **Student B** just got back from separate trips. Ask **Student B** how his or her trip was. Listen to **Student B**'s responses and comment appropriately. Now, tell **Student B** that you did the following: you toured the country, stayed in a hotel, and went to many museums.

STUDENT B   You and **Student A** just returned from separate trips. Answer **Student A**'s question about your vacation. You did the following: left your travel bag in the taxi, arrived at the airport late, and missed your flight. Listen to **Student B**'s comments. Now, ask **Student B** how his or her trip was. Listen to **Student B** and comment appropriately.
